UP AND AWAY

Contents

Cool Cat and
the Balloon — page 2

Balloon Adventures — page 14

Diana Bentley
and Sylvia Karavis

Story illustrated by
Andrés Martinez

Before Reading

In this story

 Cool Cat

 The children

Tricky words

- children
- balloon
- hurray
- stay
- road
- stuck
- whoops

Introduce these tricky words and help the reader when they come across them later!

Story starter

When Cat hears a cry for help he turns into Cool Cat. One day, Cat saw some children going on a balloon trip. Then he heard a cry for help.

Cool Cat and the Balloon

"Help!" said the children.
"The balloon is going up."

"This is a job for Cool Cat,"
said Cat.
"I will get the balloon down."

The children saw Cool Cat.

"Hurray for Cool Cat!"
said the children.
"Cool Cat will help us."

"Stay cool," said Cool Cat.
"I will get the balloon down."

7

"Hurray!" said the children.
"The balloon is going down."

8

Where have Cool Cat and the children landed?

Cool Cat got the
balloon down.
"Cool," said Cool Cat.

But then the children saw the road!

"Help!" said the children.
"We are stuck!"

"Whoops!" said Cool Cat.

Quiz

Text Detective

- Where did the balloon land?
- Why did Cool Cat say, "Whoops!"

Word Detective

- **Phonic Focus:** Initial letter sounds
  Page 3: Find a word beginning with the phoneme 'u'.
- Page 7: What words does Cool Cat say on this page?
- Page 9: Find a word meaning the opposite of 'up'.

Super Speller

Read these words:

down us got

Now try to spell them!

HA! HA! HA!

Q What does a cat like to eat on a hot day?

A Mice cream!

13

Find out about

- Flying around the world in a balloon

Tricky words

- Richard Branson
- around
- world
- dangerous
- sometimes
- desert
- Steve Fossett
- storm

Introduce these tricky words and help the reader when they come across them later!

Text starter

Richard Branson and Steve Fossett wanted to fly around the world in a balloon. But flying around the world in a balloon is very dangerous.

Balloon Adventures

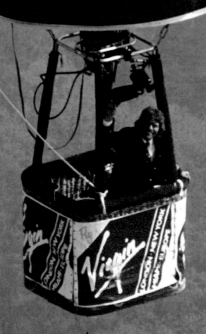

In 1998 Richard Branson wanted to fly around the world in a balloon.

But it is very dangerous to fly
around the world in a balloon.

Sometimes the balloon lands in a desert.

Sometimes the balloon lands in the sea.

Richard Branson's balloon landed in the sea!

It was very dangerous.

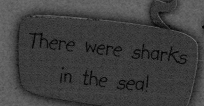

In 2001 Steve Fossett wanted
to fly around the world in
a balloon.

His balloon went over the desert and over the sea.

There was a storm but
Steve Fossett went on and on.

He went around the world.

He was the first man to fly a balloon alone around the world.

Quiz

Text Detective

- Why is it dangerous to fly around the world in a balloon?
- Would you be brave enough to try?

Word Detective

- **Phonic Focus:** Initial letter sounds

  Page 17: Find a word beginning with the phoneme 'l'.
- Page 18: Find a word that rhymes with 'me'.
- Page 21: Find the word 'over' twice on this page.

Super Speller

Read these words:

fly was but

Now try to spell them!

HA! HA! HA!

Q What happened to the two men in a balloon who had an argument?

A They fell out!